Lesson
Assessment
Book 1

Blackline Masters

Level 5

 SRA

A Division of The *McGraw-Hill* Companies

SRAonline.com

 SRA

Send all inquiries to this address:
SRA/McGraw-Hill
4400 Easton Commons
Columbus, OH 43219-6188

ISBN: 978-0-07-613227-0
MHID: 0-07-613227-7

2 3 4 5 6 7 8 9   MAZ 13 12 11 10 09 08 07

Table of Contents

Name _____ Date _____ Score _____

The Land I Lost

Vocabulary

Read each item. Fill in the bubble for the answer you think is correct.

1. What does the Latin root *spir* mean?

- Ⓐ book
- Ⓑ band
- Ⓒ breath
- Ⓓ ball

2. Lingered means about the same as

- Ⓐ watched.
- Ⓑ stayed.
- Ⓒ danced.
- Ⓓ wished.

3. People **assumed** the grandfather knew karate. **Assumed** means

- Ⓐ helped someone do something.
- Ⓑ said something nice about someone.
- Ⓒ wondered if something were true.
- Ⓓ believed something without proof.

4. According to the grandmother's **logic,** there would be bad luck next year. **Logic** has to do with

- Ⓐ the way you think.
- Ⓑ the way you treat others.
- Ⓒ how old you are.
- Ⓓ how much you like music.

5. The grandmother's plays were **inspired** by books. Being **inspired** by something means that it

- Ⓐ made you famous.
- Ⓑ had to be kept secret.
- Ⓒ gave you an idea.
- Ⓓ was unlike anything else.

The Land I Lost (continued)

Comprehension

Read the following questions carefully. Then completely fill in the bubble of each correct answer. You may look back at the selection to find the answer to each of the questions.

1. What is the first part of the selection mainly about?

Ⓐ the hunting trips in the jungle

Ⓑ the grandmother and grandfather

Ⓒ the experience of seeing an opera

Ⓓ the place where the narrator once lived

2. The narrator of this selection is

Ⓐ a man who remembers his boyhood.

Ⓑ a grandmother who loves opera.

Ⓒ a grandfather who is very shy.

Ⓓ a father who is raising a family.

The Land I Lost • **Lesson Assessment Book 1**

The Land I Lost (continued)

3. Why did the homes in the hamlet have deep trenches around them?

    (A) to protect their rice plants

    (B) to prevent water from flooding in

    (C) to keep out thieves and wild animals

    (D) to keep the children from wandering off

4. The author wrote this selection in order to

    (A) persuade readers to visit Vietnam.

    (B) tell readers about his family and life in Vietnam.

    (C) give a short history of Vietnam.

    (D) share a funny folktale from Vietnam.

5. Which of these was the most feared in the hamlet?

    (A) a man-eating tiger

    (B) a lone wild hog

    (C) a horse snake

    (D) a swamp crocodile

The Land I Lost (continued)

Read the following questions carefully. Use complete sentences to answer the questions.

6. How is the narrator's grandfather different from his grandmother?

_____

_____

7. Why did people treat the grandfather with respect?

_____

_____

8. Why does the grandmother sigh when she first sees the "Faithful One" onstage?

_____

_____

9. What are some clues that the grandmother is preparing to die at the end of the story?

_____

_____

_____

10. Why is this selection called "The Land I Lost"?

_____

_____

The Land I Lost (continued)

Read the question below. Write complete sentences for your answer. Support your answer with information from the selection.

Linking to the Concepts What do the stories reveal about the type of person the grandmother was?

_____

_____

_____

_____

_____

Read the question below. Your answer should be based on your own experience. Write complete sentences for your answer.

Personal Response How would you describe where you live to the narrator of this selection?

_____

_____

_____

_____

_____

The Land I Lost (continued)

Grammar, Usage, and Mechanics

Read each question. Fill in the bubble beside the answer in each group that is correct. If none of the answers is correct, choose the last answer, "none of the above."

1. In which sentence is a noun underlined?

  Ⓐ The zebra <u>drank</u> slowly.   Ⓒ The zebra drank <u>slowly</u>.

  Ⓑ The <u>zebra</u> drank slowly.   Ⓓ none of the above

2. In which sentence is a proper noun underlined?

  Ⓐ Uncle Ned <u>went</u> on a safari to Africa.

  Ⓑ Uncle Ned went on a <u>safari</u> to Africa.

  Ⓒ Uncle Ned went on a safari to <u>Africa</u>.

  Ⓓ none of the above

3. In which sentence is the direct object underlined?

  Ⓐ The lion chased a <u>zebra</u> through the tall grass.

  Ⓑ The lion chased a zebra <u>through</u> the tall grass.

  Ⓒ The lion chased a zebra through the <u>tall</u> grass.

  Ⓓ none of the above

4. In which sentence is an action verb underlined?

  Ⓐ The zebra <u>seemed</u> to be tiring.

  Ⓑ The lion <u>pounced</u>, but missed the zebra.

  Ⓒ The zebra <u>had</u> a chance to get away.

  Ⓓ none of the above

5. In which sentence is a linking verb underlined?

  Ⓐ The lion <u>turned</u> to look for another zebra.

  Ⓑ The zebras by the pond <u>became</u> very scared.

  Ⓒ They bounded <u>across</u> the plains.

  Ⓓ none of the above

The Land I Lost (continued)

Analyzing the Selection

Read the questions below. Write complete sentences for your answer. Support your answer with information from the selection.

Why do you think the author remembers the particular incidents described in the "The Land I Lost"? Why are certain family events in your life so easy to remember?

_____

_____

_____

_____

_____

_____

_____

_____

_____

_____

_____

The Land I Lost (continued)

Oral Fluency Assessment

Tim Sees Saturn

Tim and his mother joined the group going into the building. Tim was still a little confused about the surprise his mother mentioned, but he was also curious. The inside of the building was a huge dome. In the middle was a strange-looking device.

"This is a sixty-inch telescope," Dr. Miller told the group. "By looking through it we can view stars and planets close up." She explained that tonight they would be looking at the planet Saturn, as well as other objects in the night sky. "Why don't you go first, Tim?"

He hesitated for a minute because everyone was watching him. Finally, he put his face closer to the eyepiece. He looked through it with one eye and closed the other one. Through the telescope Tim saw a big, round, glowing planet with rings around it. Tim had seen Saturn before, but it was just a tiny light in the night sky. Now, it was many times bigger, and the rings were beautiful. "Wow! It looks so different through the telescope!" he exclaimed.

"Well," asked Mrs. Barker, holding her son's shoulders, "now would you rather we went home to watch the big game?"

"Forget the game," Tim replied. "This is great."

Name _____ Date _____ Score _____

Our Song

Vocabulary

Read each item. Fill in the bubble for the answer you think is correct.

1. The prefix **dis-** means
   - (A) before.
   - (B) not.
   - (C) too little.
   - (D) across.

2. Another word for **mist** is
   - (A) sound.
   - (B) night.
   - (C) land.
   - (D) fog.

3. When Ole Ma was young, she was **delicate**. **Delicate** means that she was
   - (A) loud and rude.
   - (B) small and weak.
   - (C) sad and lonely.
   - (D) quiet and shy.

4. The villagers **ship** peanuts all over the world. In this sentence, **ship** means
   - (A) to store something.
   - (B) to taste something.
   - (C) to plant something.
   - (D) to send something.

5. The market in this selection has a lot of **traders**. **Traders** are people who
   - (A) design and build homes.
   - (B) travel and put on shows.
   - (C) buy and sell goods.
   - (D) prepare and cook food.

Our Song (continued)

Comprehension

Read the following questions carefully. Then completely fill in the bubble of each correct answer. You may look back at the selection to find the answer to each of the questions.

1. Which of these makes the narrator like "Our Song" so much?

   Ⓐ It is from another country.

   Ⓑ It is sung by her grandmother.

   Ⓒ It is about a girl from long ago.

   Ⓓ It is in another language.

2. Which of these reminds Ole Ma of her home in Sengal?

   Ⓐ the game of basketball

   Ⓑ the sound of the wind

   Ⓒ the warmth of the sun

   Ⓓ the smells carried by the wind

Our Song (continued)

3. How are Ole Ma and the narrator alike?

   Ⓐ They both enjoy sports.

   Ⓑ They both have big feet.

   Ⓒ They both like lavender.

   Ⓓ They both are good singers.

4. Ole Ma most often sings "Our Song" when

   Ⓐ her granddaughter needs comfort.

   Ⓑ she misses her homeland.

   Ⓒ she has chores to do.

   Ⓓ her feet are being tickled.

5. How was Ole Ma's childhood different from the narrator's?

   Ⓐ She had lots of cousins.

   Ⓑ She played only with girls.

   Ⓒ She grew up in a village.

   Ⓓ She spoke one language.

Our Song (continued)

**Read the following questions carefully. Use complete
sentences to answer the questions.**

6. Why is the narrator so excited to visit Senegal?

_____

_____

7. What types of things does the narrator do with her
cousins in Senegal?

_____

_____

8. How is December in Senegal different from December
back home?

_____

_____

9. What details suggest that Ole Ma is happy to be back
in Senegal?

_____

_____

10. Why do the older village women call the narrator
Little Goat?

_____

_____

Our Song (continued)

Read the question below. Write complete sentences for your answer. Support your answer with information from the selection.

Linking to the Concepts How does visiting Senegal change the way the narrator thinks?

_____

_____

_____

_____

_____

Read the question below. Your answer should be based on your own experience. Write complete sentences for your answer.

Personal Response Is there a place that makes you feel especially happy? Describe the place.

_____

_____

_____

_____

_____

Our Song (continued)

Grammar, Usage, and Mechanics

Read each question. Fill in the bubble beside the answer in each group that is correct. If none of the answers is correct, choose the last answer, "none of the above."

1. In which sentence is the subject of the sentence underlined?
   - Ⓐ Maria <u>decorated</u> the house.
   - Ⓑ <u>Maria</u> decorated the house.
   - Ⓒ Maria decorated the <u>house</u>.
   - Ⓓ none of the above

2. Which of these is a simple sentence?
   - Ⓐ Next Friday is the start of our vacation.
   - Ⓑ We cannot go now, but we will meet soon.
   - Ⓒ After we pack, I will call you.
   - Ⓓ none of the above

3. Which of these is an interrogative sentence?
   - Ⓐ Three people forgot to take their coats after the party.
   - Ⓑ Which of these coats belongs to Jose?
   - Ⓒ Give that coat to Leon, please.
   - Ⓓ none of the above

4. Which of these is an imperative sentence?
   - Ⓐ Mom needs some help in the kitchen making lunch.
   - Ⓑ What are you doing to help?
   - Ⓒ Please wash and peel those apples.
   - Ⓓ none of the above

5. Which of these is an exclamatory sentence?
   - Ⓐ Tonight is the game.
   - Ⓒ Hooray, we won!
   - Ⓑ Are you going?
   - Ⓓ none of the above

Our Song • **Lesson Assessment Book 1**

Our Song (continued)

Analyzing the Selection

Read the question below. Write complete sentences for your answer. Support your answer with information from the selection.

What part of the selection is most like an experience you have had? Compare that part of the selection with your experience. Explain how they are alike.

_____

_____

_____

_____

_____

_____

_____

_____

_____

_____

_____

_____

Our Song (continued)

Oral Fluency Assessment

The Family Tree

"We were talking about grandparents in school today," Pam said. She sat down by her mother at the kitchen table. "How did Grandma and Grandpa meet each other, anyway?"

"I'm so happy you are interested in your family history," her mother replied, smiling. "Well, all right. They met in 1936 when they helped out on the same farm after school. Grandma's mother and father had just moved to town, and grandma didn't have many friends yet."

Pam was excited, and she asked, "How do you know all of this stuff, Mom?"

"For the past few years, your father and I have been working on our family histories," her mother answered. "We have studied our families, and we've made a family tree that goes all the way back to 1749."

"What's a family tree?" asked Pam, getting a little confused.

Pam watched as her mother drew an example of a family tree. She followed the lines her mother drew and the names she wrote. Then she listened to stories about her family. Some were funny. Others were very sad. Pam learned that she had an easier life than the people who had come before her.

"Please tell me more," Pam pleaded.

Her mother smiled. "That's enough for one night, Pam."

Name _____ Date _____ Score _____

The Dancing Bird of Paradise

Vocabulary

Read each item. Fill in the bubble for the answer you think is correct.

1. The prefix **en-** in the word *enable* means

Ⓐ to begin. Ⓒ to cause to.

Ⓑ to do again. Ⓓ to stop.

2. Another word for **startled** is

Ⓐ surprised. Ⓒ tired.

Ⓑ angry. Ⓓ puzzled.

3. Yuki's **kimono** swished and flared to the music. A **kimono** is

Ⓐ a type of Japanese dance.

Ⓑ a Japanese fan made of paper.

Ⓒ a kind of Japanese robe.

Ⓓ a Japanese dance teacher.

4. In the story, Sahomi **donned** beautiful costumes. **Donned** means

Ⓐ wished for.

Ⓑ studied.

Ⓒ sewed.

Ⓓ put on.

5. In New York City, Sahomi sometimes **soloed** as a dancer. **Soloed** means that she

Ⓐ had a difficult time earning a living.

Ⓑ performed by herself.

Ⓒ wished for a different career.

Ⓓ traveled from place to place.

The Dancing Bird of Paradise (continued)

Comprehension

Read the following questions carefully. Then completely fill in the bubble of each correct answer. You may look back at the selection to find the answer to each of the questions.

1. Why does Haruno change her name?
   - Ⓐ She plans to become a dance teacher.
   - Ⓑ She is returning to the United States.
   - Ⓒ She is honored by her dance school.
   - Ⓓ She hears that Japan may go to war.

2. In which of these places did Sahomi begin teaching?
   - Ⓐ a farm near San Francisco
   - Ⓑ a dance school in Japan
   - Ⓒ a dance school in New York City
   - Ⓓ a relocation camp in Utah

The Dancing Bird of Paradise (continued)

3. This selection is told from

    Ⓐ the second-person point of view.

    Ⓑ the third-person point of view.

    Ⓒ the first-person point of view.

    Ⓓ the point of view of Sahomi.

4. You can tell that news of Sahomi's talent spread because

    Ⓐ the wife of the president came to see her dance.

    Ⓑ she moved from Pennsylvania to New York.

    Ⓒ her costumes shone brighter than before.

    Ⓓ the American government realized its mistake.

5. The selection suggests that Sahomi dances mainly to

    Ⓐ avoid thinking about the past.

    Ⓑ keep her body fit and strong.

    Ⓒ share her culture with others.

    Ⓓ spread peace among nations.

The Dancing Bird of Paradise (continued)

Read the following questions carefully. Use complete sentences to answer the questions.

6. Why did the children not wear traditional kimonos during their first recital?

_____

_____

7. What special instructions did Sahomi give her students at the Topaz Relocation Center?

_____

_____

8. How did Sahomi help her young students picture what each dance was about?

_____

_____

9. Explain how life was different for Haruno after her cousin Yuki visited her in 1931.

_____

_____

10. What different types of dance did Sahomi study besides Japanese dance?

_____

_____

The Dancing Bird of Paradise (continued)

Read the question below. Write complete sentences for your answer. Support your answer with information from the selection.

Linking to the Concepts What types of things might Sahomi's students say about her?

_____

_____

_____

_____

_____

Read the question below. Your answer should be based on your own experience. Write complete sentences for your answer.

Personal Response If you had students, what important message would you want to teach them? Explain your answer.

_____

_____

_____

_____

_____

The Dancing Bird of Paradise (continued)

Grammar, Usage, and Mechanics

Read each question. Fill in the bubble beside the answer in each group that is correct. If none of the answers is correct, choose the last answer, "none of the above."

1. In which sentence is the adjective underlined?

   Ⓐ The tiny poodle <u>stood</u>.   Ⓒ The tiny <u>poodle</u> stood.

   Ⓑ The <u>tiny</u> poodle stood.   Ⓓ none of the above

2. In which sentence is the adjective used correctly?

   Ⓐ Xavia is the more beautiful town we visited.

   Ⓑ Xavia is the most beautifulest town we visited.

   Ⓒ Xavia is the most beautiful town we visited.

   Ⓓ none of the above

3. Which sentence is a declarative sentence?

   Ⓐ The swimmers raced quickly across the pool.

   Ⓑ Who is in the lead?

   Ⓒ Vida won the meet!

   Ⓓ none of the above

4. In which sentence is the adverb used correctly?

   Ⓐ The crowd cheered loudly for the winner.

   Ⓑ The crowd cheered most loud for the winner.

   Ⓒ The crowd cheered more louder for the winner.

   Ⓓ none of the above

5. In which sentence is the word modified by an adverb underlined?

   Ⓐ The <u>furry</u> hamster raced wildly in his turning wheel.

   Ⓑ The furry hamster raced wildly in his <u>turning</u> wheel.

   Ⓒ The furry hamster raced <u>wildly</u> in his turning wheel.

   Ⓓ none of the above

The Dancing Bird of Paradise (continued)

Analyzing the Selection

Read the question below. Write complete sentences for your answer. Support your answer with information from the selections.

Think about the selections "The Land I Lost," "Our Song," and "The Dancing Bird of Paradise." What do the selections say about the importance of heritage?

_____

_____

_____

_____

_____

_____

_____

_____

_____

_____

_____

The Dancing Bird of Paradise (continued)

Oral Fluency Assessment

A Prized Possession

Dad rose from his seat and walked to Thomas's chair. "Son, I have been waiting for your birthday to give you a very special gift. My father gave these stamps to me when I was about your age. This collection has been one of my most cherished possessions, and now I want to give it to you." He placed a dusty shoe box in front of Thomas.

Thomas untied the frayed string and opened the lid of the box. Inside he found several yellowed envelopes stuffed full. Under the envelopes was a thin book. He opened the book and discovered page after page of postage stamps.

Thomas attempted to appear excited about his gift, but he did not understand what was so great about a box of old stamps. "Thanks," he said, with a forced smile.

Then he noticed that Tammy had taken the box. She was looking in each envelope. "Look at this one!" she exclaimed. "It's from the year I was born. Hey, Thomas, that's the year you were born, too!"

Thomas began to understand why the box was so important to his father and grandfather. He moved over by Tammy so that he could see the stamps better. Twenty minutes later, he did not even notice that his ice cream had melted all over his birthday cake.

Name _____ Date _____ Score _____

From Miss Ida's Porch

Vocabulary

Read each item. Fill in the bubble for the answer you think is correct.

1. **Spellbound** means
   - Ⓐ sleepy.
   - Ⓑ secretive.
   - Ⓒ doubtful.
   - Ⓓ fascinated.

2. What is one meaning of the suffix *-ant?*
   - Ⓐ characterized by
   - Ⓑ one who does
   - Ⓒ full of
   - Ⓓ without

3. Daddy attended a **concert** at the Lincoln Memorial. In this sentence, **concert** means
   - Ⓐ a music performance.
   - Ⓑ a family reunion.
   - Ⓒ a storytelling event.
   - Ⓓ a presidential speech.

4. Constitution Hall is called the **forbidden** hall. If a place is **forbidden,** it means
   - Ⓐ you do not know how to get there.
   - Ⓑ special events are held there.
   - Ⓒ history was made there.
   - Ⓓ you are not allowed there.

5. When telling a story, Uncle Henry would **claim** the floor. In this sentence, **claim** means
   - Ⓐ shout something out loud.
   - Ⓑ take something as your own.
   - Ⓒ disagree with something.
   - Ⓓ complain about something.

From Miss Ida's Porch (continued)

Comprehension

Read the following questions carefully. Then completely fill in the bubble of each correct answer. You may look back at the selection to find the answer to each of the questions.

1. Why is Miss Ida's porch special?

Ⓐ It is the nicest porch in the neighborhood.

Ⓑ Neighbors gather there to share stories.

Ⓒ There is always something to eat there.

Ⓓ Famous people used to meet there.

2. Daddy takes a seat on the porch because

Ⓐ Shoo Kate has agreed to tell her story again.

Ⓑ Miss Ida brings a chair just for him.

Ⓒ he wants to tell a tale about Uncle Henry.

Ⓓ he has to keep an eye on his children.

UNIT 1 · Lesson 4

From Miss Ida's Porch (continued)

3. Daddy begins to breathe loud and hard because he is

   Ⓐ angry about how African Americans were treated.

   Ⓑ tired after walking up Miss Ida's porch steps.

   Ⓒ annoyed with how Sylvia is acting.

   Ⓓ sad when he remembers Uncle Henry.

4. Which of these stories is told last?

   Ⓐ Shoo Kate's story about seeing Marian Anderson.

   Ⓑ Uncle Henry's story about the Lincoln Memorial.

   Ⓒ Daddy's story about what made Uncle Henry special.

   Ⓓ Daddy's story about Marian Anderson's last concert.

5. Which of these is a fact about Uncle Henry, and not an opinion?

   Ⓐ He was everyone's favorite.

   Ⓑ He was one of the lucky ones.

   Ⓒ He was over six feet tall.

   Ⓓ He was a grand old guy.

UNIT 1 **Lesson 4**

From Miss Ida's Porch (continued)

Read the following questions carefully. Use complete sentences to answer the questions.

6. What are some ways Daddy is like his Uncle Henry?

_____

_____

7. What does the narrator mean when she says, "My dad's story brought the end to the very best time that evening"?

_____

_____

8. How can you tell that Daddy's story is "fuel" for the narrator's young mind?

_____

_____

9. According to Uncle Henry, what helps you to know where you are going?

_____

_____

10. What does the narrator see and hear just before she drifts off to sleep?

_____

_____

From Miss Ida's Porch • **Lesson Assessment Book 1**

From Miss Ida's Porch (continued)

Read the question below. Write complete sentences for your answer. Support your answer with information from the selection.

Linking to the Concepts How are the people on Ida's porch sharing their history?

_____

_____

_____

_____

_____

Read the question below. Your answer should be based on your own experience. Write complete sentences for your answer.

Personal Response What story might you or another family member tell on Ida's porch? Explain why this story is so important to your family.

_____

_____

_____

_____

_____

From Miss Ida's Porch (continued)

Grammar, Usage, and Mechanics

Read each question. Fill in the bubble beside the answer in each group that is correct. If none of the answers is correct, choose the last answer, "none of the above."

1. Which sentence has correct punctuation?

Ⓐ Pie, cake, and cookies, are for sale.

Ⓑ Pie, cake, and cookies are for sale.

Ⓒ Pie, cake and cookies are for sale.

Ⓓ none of the above

2. Which sentence has correct punctuation?

Ⓐ After the, rain the air smelled fresh and clean.

Ⓑ After the rain the air, smelled fresh and clean.

Ⓒ After the rain, the air smelled fresh and clean.

Ⓓ none of the above

3. Which sentence has correct punctuation?

Ⓐ The band came into town last, and the parade ended.

Ⓑ The band came into town last and the parade ended.

Ⓒ The band came into town last and, the parade ended.

Ⓓ none of the above

4. Which sentence is correct?

Ⓐ "Practice your scales every day" She said.

Ⓑ "practice your scales every day", she said.

Ⓒ "Practice your scales every day," she said.

Ⓓ none of the above

5. Which item has correct capitalization?

Ⓐ Akron, Ohio

Ⓑ akron, ohio

Ⓒ Akron, ohio

Ⓓ none of the above

From Miss Ida's Porch (continued)

Analyzing the Selection

Read the questions below. Write complete sentences for your answer. Support your answer with information from the selection.

Why are places like Ida's porch so important to people? Do you think these places have been important to people throughout history?

_____

_____

_____

_____

_____

_____

_____

_____

_____

_____

_____

_____

_____

From Miss Ida's Porch (continued)

Oral Fluency Assessment

Going to Work with Mom

Traci was lucky. Although some of her friends dreaded "Take Your Child to Work Day," Traci enjoyed it. Her mother worked for the city parks department, so her job often took her outdoors.

This morning the two of them were walking through a strip of park that separated the river from the city. Bicyclists whizzed past.

"Here we are," Traci's mother said, pointing to a building up ahead. "That's the reason we're here."

Because the parks department usually dealt with landscaping and trails, Traci was puzzled. Her mother explained that the building was owned by the city. It had once been a restaurant.

"After the restaurant moved out, we bought the building. Our job today is to brainstorm ways to use it," her mother said.

The two walked around the building. As bikes continued to stream past, Traci asked, "We have a lot of bicycle riders in town, don't we?"

"We're one of the nation's leaders," her mother said proudly.

Traci said, "All those people riding to work downtown might need a place to shower and change into their work clothes. Could this building be used for that?"

Her mother nodded, "Maybe it could be a repair shop with bicycle storage, too."

"Great minds think alike, Mom," Traci said. "It's a good thing I came with you today!"

Name _____ Date _____ Score _____

In Two Worlds

Vocabulary

Read each item. Fill in the bubble for the answer you think is correct.

1. What is one meaning of the suffix *-ence?*

  Ⓐ without   Ⓒ wrongly

  Ⓑ full of   Ⓓ quality or state

2. Another word for **inhabit** is

  Ⓐ live.   Ⓒ question.

  Ⓑ understand.   Ⓓ move.

3. The Alaskan tundra is **vast.** If something is **vast,** it is

  Ⓐ without human life.

  Ⓑ frozen year-round.

  Ⓒ very great in size.

  Ⓓ in need of protection.

4. The students want to be **fluent** in English and Yup'ik. **Fluent** means

  Ⓐ able to speak easily.

  Ⓑ able to teach others.

  Ⓒ able to write books.

  Ⓓ able to visit an area.

5. When the weather grew cold, the plants **withered. Withered** means that the plants

  Ⓐ leaned toward the sun.

  Ⓑ became dry and wilted.

  Ⓒ sent roots down deep.

  Ⓓ grow straight and strong.

In Two Worlds (continued)

Comprehension

Read the following questions carefully. Then completely fill in the bubble of each correct answer. You may look back at the selection to find the answer to each of the questions.

1. What does it mean that the Yup'ik Eskimo moved "with the seasons"?

Ⓐ They had to follow the sun in order to stay warm.

Ⓑ They grew bored if they stayed in one place too long.

Ⓒ They went to where food or game was available.

Ⓓ They traveled only during traditional holidays.

2. What is something Alice does that her mother did not do?

Ⓐ She bakes bread on a wood stove.

Ⓑ She has a paying job.

Ⓒ She spends most evenings telling stories.

Ⓓ She teaches her girls how to sew.

In Two Worlds (continued)

3. What do the Rivers children have that their parents did not have?

Ⓐ the chance to learn English

Ⓑ the opportunity to go fishing

Ⓒ the chance to attend school

Ⓓ the ability to watch television

4. How is Scammon Bay different today from how it used to be?

Ⓐ It has more contact with the outside world.

Ⓑ It has fewer people living in it.

Ⓒ It has a greater variety of wildlife.

Ⓓ It has one big school instead of many little schools.

5. Which of the Yup'ik traditions has remained with the Rivers family?

Ⓐ living in a home made out of sod

Ⓑ fishing and hunting for food

Ⓒ burning seal oil lamps for light

Ⓓ sitting on the floor while eating

In Two Worlds (continued)

Read the following questions carefully. Use complete sentences to answer the questions.

6. How has the arrival of planes changed life in Scammon Bay?

_____

_____

7. How has education changed over the years in Scammon Bay?

_____

_____

8. What does the author mean by "Their mark on the land was light"?

_____

_____

9. How is Billy a teacher to his children?

_____

_____

10. What skills do the Rivers think their children need in order to survive in a fast-changing Scammon Bay?

_____

_____

In Two Worlds (continued)

Read the questions below. Write complete sentences for your answer. Support your answer with information from the selection.

Linking to the Concepts Has life improved in Scammon Bay? Why or why not?

_____

_____

_____

_____

_____

Read the question below. Your answer should be based on your own experience. Write complete sentences for your answer.

Personal Response How is your life different from your parents' and grandparents' childhoods? Give examples of how they are different.

_____

_____

_____

_____

_____

In Two Worlds (continued)

Grammar, Usage, and Mechanics

Read each question. Fill in the bubble beside the answer in each group that is correct. If none of the answers is correct, choose the last answer, "none of the above."

1. In which sentence is a proper noun underlined?

  Ⓐ We took a <u>trip</u> to Florida.   Ⓒ We <u>took</u> a trip to Florida.

  Ⓑ We took a trip to <u>Florida</u>.   Ⓓ none of the above

2. Which sentence is correct?

  Ⓐ When Aunt Leah arrives, we will begin a long tour of Key West.

  Ⓑ She and Uncle ted is driving from New Jersey.

  Ⓒ They plan to stop brief in north Carolina and Georgia.

  Ⓓ none of the above

3. Which of these is a simple sentence?

  Ⓐ The frog leaped, but the fly got away.

  Ⓑ The big, green frog was hungry and tired.

  Ⓒ After some time had gone by, another fly flew past.

  Ⓓ none of the above

4. Which sentence has a compound predicate?

  Ⓐ The fly buzzed by a second time.

  Ⓑ This surprised the frog, but he flicked out his tongue.

  Ⓒ The frog jumped and splashed into the pond.

  Ⓓ none of the above

5. Which of these is an imperative sentence?

  Ⓐ Give the paper to the student behind you.

  Ⓑ It is my turn to speak!

  Ⓒ Was the man on the left here first?

  Ⓓ none of the above

In Two Worlds (continued)

Analyzing the Selection

Read the question below. Write complete sentences for your answer. Support your answer with information from the selection.

In the selection "In Two Worlds," the Rivers family lives in the same area their family has inhabited for thousands of years. How do you think this affects family traditions?

_____

_____

_____

_____

_____

_____

_____

_____

_____

_____

In Two Worlds (continued)

Oral Fluency Assessment

A Trunk Full of Treasures

Something about closed or locked boxes had always intrigued Megan. So when her father pushed a dusty trunk from the back of the garage to get at a bicycle that was hung on the wall, Megan's eyes lit up.

"Hey, what's in there?"

Megan's father turned to her. He wiped his hands on his jeans. "I think it has your mother's old high school yearbooks in it. Old photos, things like that." He waved his hand.

Megan's father wiped cobwebs off the bicycle. Megan ran over and popped open the trunk's heavy lid. The trunk gave off a musty but not unpleasant odor. And, just as Megan's father had guessed, it was full of yearbooks, framed pictures, and other keepsakes from decades ago.

In other words, for someone like Megan, it was a treasure chest! Megan pulled a yearbook out and leafed through it. She kept her eyes peeled for pictures of her mother. But the photos of so many teenagers distracted her. And to think that these kids were now all adults!

Then Megan saw a picture of a student speaking at an assembly. Though the hairstyle and clothing were unfamiliar to Megan, it was clearly her mother.

"Dad, look!" Megan said.

Glancing over, her father asked, "You didn't know that your mom was president of the student body?"

Name _____ **Date** _____ **Score** _____

Narrative Writing

Writing Situation
A tradition in your family

Audience
Other students your age

Directions for Writing
Families have lots of traditions. Some of them have to do with special days, while others are about the family's past. Write a story about a tradition in your family. Try to write the story from the third-person point of view as if you were an outside observer.

Checklist
You will earn the best score if you
- think about the tradition and plan your writing before you begin.
- remember who will read your story.
- write in a way that is interesting to your readers.
- make sure your ideas flow in a way that makes sense.
- describe the tradition so the reader can understand it.
- use words that tell how you feel about the tradition.
- include enough details so the reader will understand the tradition.
- use correct capital letters, punctuation, and spelling.
- use subjects, verbs, and modifiers correctly.
- read your writing after you finish and check for mistakes.

_____

_____

_____

_____

_____

_____

_____

_____

_____

_____

_____

_____

_____

_____

_____

_____

_____

Name _____ **Date** _____ **Score** _____

The Sparks Fly

Vocabulary

Read each item. Fill in the bubble for the answer you think is correct.

1. What is the meaning of the prefix *in-?*

   Ⓐ half   Ⓒ before

   Ⓑ not   Ⓓ under

2. Another word for **dissolve** is

   Ⓐ pour.   Ⓒ spark.

   Ⓑ spread.   Ⓓ mix.

3. The scientist gave a **demonstration** on electricity. A **demonstration**

   Ⓐ discovers something new.

   Ⓑ fixes something that is broken.

   Ⓒ creates something as a team.

   Ⓓ shows how something works.

4. The Library Company received many strange objects from **donors. Donors** are people who

   Ⓐ ask important questions.

   Ⓑ give things away.

   Ⓒ want an education.

   Ⓓ are looking for work.

5. Heating systems in the 1700s were **inefficient.** If something is **inefficient,** it

   Ⓐ is unpopular.   Ⓒ works poorly.

   Ⓑ makes noise.   Ⓓ costs little.

The Sparks Fly (continued)

Comprehension

Read the following questions carefully. Then completely fill in the bubble of each correct answer. You may look back at the selection to find the answer to each of the questions.

1. In this selection, what seems to interest Franklin the most?

(A) becoming a wealthy person

(B) learning how things work

(C) earning world-wide fame

(D) helping those in need

2. The Library Company's first exhibition was

(A) Thomas Penn's print of an orrery.

(B) John Penn's air pump.

(C) Franklin's cork spider.

(D) a Leyden jar.

The Sparks Fly (continued)

3. What effect did Franklin's cork spider have on visitors?

   Ⓐ It gave them a mild electrical shock.

   Ⓑ It caused their hair to stand up.

   Ⓒ It sent a spark from their fingers.

   Ⓓ It made them jump in surprise.

4. Which of these helped Franklin discover that electricity was either *positive* or *negative*?

   Ⓐ People acted differently around demonstrations of electricity.

   Ⓑ Objects with an electric charge pushed away or attracted things.

   Ⓒ Sparks would fly out and make a hiss, crackle, and pop sound.

   Ⓓ Jars linked together with brass thread could cause electrical shock.

5. According to the selection, why did Franklin write *Experiments and Other Observations on Electricity Made at Philadelphia in America?*

   Ⓐ to share his discoveries with other scientists

   Ⓑ to claim that he had invented electricity

   Ⓒ to attract more people to his demonstrations

   Ⓓ to tell funny stories about his experiments

The Sparks Fly (continued)

Read the following questions carefully. Use complete sentences to answer the questions.

6. What details from the selection show that Franklin liked to have fun?

_____

_____

7. What is the purpose of all the questions in the first paragraph?

_____

_____

8. Where did Franklin get information to satisfy his curiosity?

_____

_____

9. What types of things did the Library Company have when it moved to the second floor of the new State House?

_____

_____

10. How did Franklin's interest in electricity compare with his interest in other subjects?

_____

_____

The Sparks Fly (continued)

Read the question below. Write complete sentences for your answer. Support your answer with information from the selection.

Linking to the Concepts How was Franklin's work with electricity important?

_____

_____

_____

_____

_____

Read the question below. Your answer should be based on your own experience. Write complete sentences for your answer.

Personal Response Which of the demonstrations described in the selection would you most liked to have attended? Explain your choice.

_____

_____

_____

_____

_____

The Sparks Fly (continued)

Grammar, Usage, and Mechanics

Read each question. Fill in the bubble beside the answer in each group that is correct. If none of the answers is correct, choose the last answer, "none of the above."

1. Which sentence has correct punctuation?

    (A) Five o'clock is when the city's only train arrives.

    (B) Five o'clock is when the citys only train arrives.

    (C) Five o'clock is when the citys' only train arrives.

    (D) none of the above

2. Which sentence has correct punctuation?

    (A) The lilies petals began to drop on the table.

    (B) The lilie's petals began to drop on the table.

    (C) The lilies's petals began to drop on the table.

    (D) none of the above

3. In which sentence is a plural noun underlined?

    (A) The <u>boss</u> answered the phone and yelled for Tom.

    (B) In the <u>garden</u>, we grew tomatoes, onions, and peas.

    (C) The brown <u>puppies</u> slept in a box by the fireplace.

    (D) none of the above

4. Which sentence has correct plural forms?

    (A) The friends all brought their lunchs to the park.

    (B) Please pick up all the stickes and stones in the yard.

    (C) Most small towns have at least two mailboxes.

    (D) none of the above

5. Which is an example of an action verb?

    (A) am   (C) will

    (B) throw   (D) none of the above

The Sparks Fly • **Lesson Assessment Book 1**

The Sparks Fly (continued)

Analyzing the Selection

Read the questions below. Write complete sentences for your answer. Support your answer with information from the selection.

What do you think people thought of Franklin during his life? Why do you think they thought this way?

_____

_____

_____

_____

_____

_____

_____

_____

_____

_____

_____

_____

_____

The Sparks Fly (continued)

Oral Fluency Assessment

Emerson's Adventure

Emerson rode with her mother and little sister in the family station wagon. Her father and brother were behind them in the truck with the big, black tubes piled in the back. With each passing mile, Emerson smiled more and more. She imagined the fun and excitement they would have. They would float down the river splashing each other and looking at the nature around them. They finally reached Tom's Fork and parked the car. Emerson jumped out quickly. She could not wait for the adventure to start.

"Not so fast, Emerson," said her mother. "Remember, we're just here to leave the car. We still have to drive up the river. After we float back here, we'll be able to drive the car upstream to the truck."

"Oh, yeah, false alarm," Emerson said. She had forgotten the family's plan to leave one car at each end of the float.

Once the whole family was in the truck, they set out for Jenkins Bar, a sandy beach on a wide part of the river. It did not take very long to get there on the road. But because the river has many winding turns and the current is kind of slow, it was going to take them about three hours to float back to Tom's Fork. "That's three wonderful hours of tubing," thought Emerson.

The Sparks Fly • **Lesson Assessment Book 1**

Name _____ Date _____ Score _____

Tailing Tornadoes

Vocabulary

Read each item. Fill in the bubble for the answer you think is correct.

1. Another word for **severe** is
   - Ⓐ dangerous.
   - Ⓒ quiet.
   - Ⓑ quick.
   - Ⓓ smooth.

2. Which word contains the Latin root meaning "to see"?
   - Ⓐ credible
   - Ⓒ television
   - Ⓑ sense
   - Ⓓ science

3. Tornadoes are **raging** columns of wind. What does **raging** mean in this sentence?
   - Ⓐ curved and rounded
   - Ⓑ long and narrow
   - Ⓒ amazing and thrilling
   - Ⓓ active and powerful

4. Greg took a **survey** of the morning sky. In this sentence, a **survey** is
   - Ⓐ a travel map.
   - Ⓒ a quick drawing.
   - Ⓑ a careful look.
   - Ⓓ a scientific question.

5. As a meteorologist, Greg thinks tornadoes are an **inspiration.** An **inspiration** is
   - Ⓐ a stirring of the mind.
   - Ⓑ a dangerous experiment.
   - Ⓒ a problem with nature.
   - Ⓓ a strange hobby.

Tailing Tornadoes (continued)

Comprehension

Read the following questions carefully. Then completely fill in the bubble of each correct answer. You may look back at the selection to find the answer to each of the questions.

1. The main reason Greg chases tornadoes is

  Ⓐ because experiencing tornadoes is exciting.

  Ⓑ so people can know more about tornadoes.

  Ⓒ so tornadoes can someday be prevented.

  Ⓓ because tornadoes are his hobby.

2. Which two things help to form cumulonimbus clouds or thunderheads?

  Ⓐ tornadoes and twisters

  Ⓑ warm air and cool air

  Ⓒ spirals and stovepipes

  Ⓓ storms and storm chasers

Tailing Tornadoes (continued)

3. Why does Greg pick up Bill on his way to the target area?

Ⓐ He knows that it is safer to chase in pairs.

Ⓑ He wants to show Bill an example of chasing.

Ⓒ He needs someone to photograph the chase.

Ⓓ He thinks Bill knows his way around Texas.

4. What is the first clue that Greg and Bill are getting close to the tornado?

Ⓐ They see a wall cloud start to swirl.

Ⓑ They notice anvil clouds forming.

Ⓒ They see some cumulonimbus clouds.

Ⓓ They watch a funnel cloud start to form.

5. The author most likely wrote this selection to

Ⓐ compare a tornado with a twister.

Ⓑ share a tornado tale from long ago.

Ⓒ explain how to survive a tornado.

Ⓓ inform readers about tornadoes and their study.

Tailing Tornadoes (continued)

Read the following questions carefully. Use complete sentences to answer the questions.

6. What helps to make a vortex visible?

_____

_____

7. What is the ham radio used for during a chase?

_____

_____

_____

8. Why do some tornadoes make noise and others do not?

_____

_____

9. Why does the author write that the tornado starts to "rope out" before disappearing?

_____

_____

10. On the lines below, write one fact about tornadoes from the selection.

_____

_____

Tailing Tornadoes (continued)

Read the question below. Write complete sentences for your answer. Support your answer with information from the selection.

Linking to the Concepts If being hit by a tornado is not the main threat to storm chasers, what *is* the main threat?

_____

_____

_____

_____

_____

Read the questions below. Your answer should be based on your own experience. Write complete sentences for your answer.

Personal Response Would you like to be a storm chaser? Why?

_____

_____

_____

_____

_____

Tailing Tornadoes (continued)

Grammar, Usage, and Mechanics

Read each question. Fill in the bubble beside the answer in each group that is correct. If none of the answers is correct, choose the last answer, "none of the above."

1. When you search for information with a computer, which of these is most helpful?

Ⓐ a comma   Ⓒ a keyword

Ⓑ a rhyme   Ⓓ none of the above

2. Which Internet site would probably give you the best information about Yellowstone National Park?

Ⓐ the National Center on Education

Ⓑ the National High School Athletic Association

Ⓒ the National Park Service

Ⓓ none of the above

3. If you searched for "pet fish," which of these would you probably find?

Ⓐ goldfish   Ⓒ dolphins

Ⓑ whales   Ⓓ none of the above

4. Which search words would help you find news in other countries?

Ⓐ school news   Ⓒ local news

Ⓑ world news   Ⓓ none of the above

5. Which sentence contains a coordinating conjunction?

Ⓐ Before you go, leave me the book.

Ⓑ I did the laundry, and Jack folded clothes.

Ⓒ We went into the library.

Ⓓ none of the above

Tailing Tornadoes (continued)

Analyzing the Selection

Read the question below. Write complete sentences for your answer. Support your answer with information from the selection.

Do you think storm chasers are real scientists whose work helps people? Explain your opinion thoroughly.

_____

_____

_____

_____

_____

_____

_____

_____

_____

_____

_____

_____

_____

_____

Tailing Tornadoes (continued)

Oral Fluency Assessment

The Cell Phone

As they walked to the movie theater, Russell and Patricia talked about film. Russell wanted to see a mystery, but Patricia was voting for science fiction.

"Listen to that," said Russell, looking around. A small voice was coming from under the nearby hedges.

Bending down, Patricia and Russell heard the voice say, "To listen to your messages, press the star button." The voice was from a cell phone!

Patricia found the phone and said, "Someone must have lost this. How do we figure out who the owner is?"

The two were stumped, and then Patricia suggested, "Russell, find the list of numbers in the cell phone."

"Okay," said Russell, "but I doubt the owner is listed there."

"Now look for a listing for 'ICE' and call that number," Patricia said.

Scrolling through the menu, Russell exclaimed, "Hey! How did you know ICE would be listed here?"

Patricia explained that ICE stood for *In Case of Emergency*.

Nodding, Russell called ICE, and a man answered. Russell explained that he had found the phone and asked the man if he knew whose phone it was.

The man said, "Thank you, so much! My daughter has been looking everywhere for it." He then told Russell that he would meet him at the movie theater shortly.

Name _____ Date _____ Score _____

Jake Drake Know-It-All

Vocabulary

Read each item. Fill in the bubble for the answer you think is correct.

1. What word best completes the following word relationship?

_____, **theory, scientific method**

- Ⓐ newspaper
- Ⓑ animals
- Ⓒ light
- Ⓓ hypothesis

2. Another word for **practically** is

- Ⓐ really.
- Ⓑ nearly.
- Ⓒ carefully.
- Ⓓ neatly.

3. To finish their science project, the boys must write their **conclusions.** In this sentence, **conclusions** are

- Ⓐ why an experiment was needed.
- Ⓑ how an experiment was done.
- Ⓒ what is learned from an experiment.
- Ⓓ who is in charge of an experiment.

4. Willie **squinted** when Jake said something puzzling. **Squinted** means that he

- Ⓐ made a strange sound.
- Ⓑ closed his eyes partway.
- Ⓒ waved his arms.
- Ⓓ sat down and thought.

5. Willie wanted to **observe** how different balls bounced. In this sentence, **observe** means

- Ⓐ to practice a new skill.
- Ⓑ to teach others.
- Ⓒ to change something.
- Ⓓ to make a careful study.

Jake Drake Know-It-All (continued)

Comprehension

Read the following questions carefully. Then completely fill in the bubble of each correct answer. You may look back at the selection to find the answer to each of the questions.

1. Which statement is true about Jake's dad?

   Ⓐ He works at the school.

   Ⓑ He wants to be helpful.

   Ⓒ He knows all about electromagnets.

   Ⓓ He thinks his own ideas are best.

2. Jake persuades Mrs. Snavin to let Willie be his partner by

   Ⓐ pointing out the rules in the science fair booklet.

   Ⓑ promising to do an excellent science fair project.

   Ⓒ telling her that his current partner is sick.

   Ⓓ saying that they had already been working together.

Jake Drake Know-It-All (continued)

3. Willie is surprised when Jake tells him they are partners because Willie thought Jake had

Ⓐ started with another partner.

Ⓑ thought the ball idea was silly.

Ⓒ wanted to work by himself.

Ⓓ waited until the last week.

4. Why does Jake think he and Willie are like magnets?

Ⓐ They stick together.

Ⓑ They like junkyards.

Ⓒ They are drawn to sports.

Ⓓ They laugh at the same stuff.

5. The cans were useful in the boys' project for all of these reasons EXCEPT

Ⓐ they had weights on them.

Ⓑ they were made of steel.

Ⓒ they could be stacked together.

Ⓓ they contained food.

Jake Drake Know-It-All (continued)

Read the following questions carefully. Use complete sentences to answer the questions.

6. What was the first step in Jake and Willie's science fair project?

_____

_____

7. How does Jake finally make his father feel included?

_____

_____

8. What does Jake think of his friend Willie?

_____

_____

9. What is a fact about Mrs. Karp? What is an opinion about Mrs. Drinkwater?

_____

_____

10. Why do you think the author ends the selection the way that he does?

_____

_____

Jake Drake Know-It-All (continued)

Read the question below. Write complete sentences for your answer. Support your answer with information from the selection.

Linking to the Concepts In what ways is Jake a good leader?

_____

_____

_____

_____

_____

_____

Read the question below. Your answer should be based on your own experience. Write complete sentences for your answer.

Personal Response Would you like to be Jake's partner? Explain your answer using details from the selection.

_____

_____

_____

_____

_____

Jake Drake Know-It-All (continued)

Grammar, Usage, and Mechanics

Read each question. Fill in the bubble beside the answer in each group that is correct. If none of the answers is correct, choose the last answer, "none of the above."

1. Which sentence contains a pronoun?

Ⓐ Wanda and I are planning to go along too.

Ⓑ How many people is Jacob going to take?

Ⓒ Three more people can ride in the van.

Ⓓ none of the above

2. Which sentence contains a possessive pronoun?

Ⓐ The suitcases should fit.

Ⓑ That suitcase is mine.

Ⓒ Can you get the car packed?

Ⓓ none of the above

3. Which sentence contains a subject pronoun?

Ⓐ We are not ready to leave yet.

Ⓑ Give Jacob his suitcase to carry.

Ⓒ Her suitcases are over there.

Ⓓ none of the above

4. Which sentence contains an object pronoun?

Ⓐ Mia and her sister went with Tina.

Ⓑ Mia's sister forgot her dress shoes.

Ⓒ Tina lent her a pair of shoes.

Ⓓ none of the above

5. Which pronoun can take the place of the underlined part in this sentence?

<u>Tristan and I</u> were upset because we could not go.

Ⓐ We

Ⓑ He

Ⓒ Us

Ⓓ none of the above

Jake Drake Know-It-All (continued)

Analyzing the Selection

Read the questions below. Write complete sentences for your answer. Support your answer with information from the selections.

What types of traits do you need to be a scientist? Why? Support your answer with information from the selections you have read in this unit.

_____

_____

_____

_____

_____

_____

_____

_____

_____

_____

_____

_____

_____

Jake Drake Know-It-All (continued)

Oral Fluency Assessment

Meeting a New Friend

"May I sit here?" asked Roger in an unusual voice. He signed while he talked. It was a little difficult to understand him.

"Sure," answered Patsy. She was very nervous. Her words barely came out. "What am I supposed to do?" she asked herself. "I've never met a hearing-impaired person before."

All that morning, Patsy had a hard time paying attention. She kept looking over at Roger. He seemed to be able to understand what was going on in class. "How does he do that?" she wondered to herself.

At lunch, Roger sat beside Patsy. Her two friends, Amos and Tara, were there also. Roger smiled and started talking. It was difficult for them at first. But by the end of lunch, they knew a little bit more about each other.

That afternoon, Mrs. Martin took some time to let Roger and the other students get to know each other better. Patsy was surprised to find that one of her other friends, Kyle, actually knew sign language. Patsy also found herself trying to explain what Roger was saying when the others couldn't understand.

That afternoon, Roger and Patsy walked home together for a few blocks. Patsy learned some signs. She told Roger about her family. By the time she reached the corner of her street, she was able to sign "good-bye."

Name _____ Date _____ Score _____

The Wind at Work

Vocabulary

Read each item. Fill in the bubble for the answer you think is correct.

1. If something **expands,** it becomes

Ⓐ larger.   Ⓒ louder.

Ⓑ softer.   Ⓓ faster.

2. What does the prefix **re-** mean?

Ⓐ into   Ⓒ again

Ⓑ not   Ⓓ down from

3. The **flickering** lanterns could be seen during the storm. **Flickering** means

Ⓐ shining extra brightly.

Ⓑ going on and off quickly.

Ⓒ banging against each other.

Ⓓ bouncing up and down.

4. The wind helps to **propel** sailboats on the water. To **propel** something means to

Ⓐ protect it.   Ⓒ move it forward.

Ⓑ anchor it.   Ⓓ keep it balanced.

5. A set of turbines **converts** wind energy into electricity. In this sentence, **converts** means

Ⓐ stores something for future use.

Ⓑ makes something out of nothing.

Ⓒ traps something and gets rid of it safely.

Ⓓ changes something into something else.

The Wind at Work (continued)

Comprehension

Read the following questions carefully. Then completely fill in the bubble of each correct answer. You may look back at the selection to find the answer to each of the questions.

1. The Dutch most likely called the sea the Waterwolf because

(A) the sea was shaped like a wolf.

(B) the sea was threatening like a wolf.

(C) the sea sounded like a wolf.

(D) the sea moved like a wolf.

2. Which of these devices was the first to harness the power of the wind?

(A) kites

(B) turbines

(C) sailboats

(D) windmills

The Wind at Work (continued)

3. Wind is caused by

Ⓐ the sun warming Earth unevenly.

Ⓑ the turning of windmill sails.

Ⓒ the rotation of Earth.

Ⓓ the great distance between the equator and the poles.

4. The selection suggests that wind is not a perfect source of energy because

Ⓐ it is costly to harness.

Ⓑ it is not as abundant as coal.

Ⓒ it causes damage.

Ⓓ it is difficult to predict the amount of wind.

5. According to the selection, why were windmills so popular?

Ⓐ They were a sign of wealth.

Ⓑ They made heavy jobs easier.

Ⓒ They were easy to transport.

Ⓓ They helped predict weather.

The Wind at Work (continued)

Read the following questions carefully. Use complete sentences to answer the questions.

6. What would be the effect of having wind turbines produce ten percent of America's electrical power?

_____

_____

7. What does it mean when the author writes that wind is a "renewable energy"?

_____

_____

8. According to the author, what do today's wind turbines look like?

_____

_____

9. What are two reasons the wind is a good source of energy?

_____

_____

10. What replaced the windmill in Europe in the 1800s?

_____

_____

The Wind at Work (continued)

Read the question below. Write complete sentences for your answer. Support your answer with information from the selection.

Linking to the Concepts How has wind been valuable to people throughout history?

_____

_____

_____

_____

_____

_____

Read the questions below. Your answer should be based on your own experience. Write complete sentences for your answer.

Personal Response Do you like being outside when it is windy? Why or why not?

_____

_____

_____

_____

_____

_____

The Wind at Work (continued)

Grammar, Usage, and Mechanics

Read each question. Fill in the bubble beside the answer in each group that is correct. If none of the answers is correct, choose the last answer, "none of the above."

1. Which of these is a compound sentence?

Ⓐ The carnival is held on the town playground every year.

Ⓑ Many groups and individuals set up stands there.

Ⓒ The children enjoy the rides, and the adults buy crafts.

Ⓓ none of the above

2. Which of these is a compound sentence?

Ⓐ Everyone loves the many choices food stands offer.

Ⓑ After dark, the lights on the Ferris wheel come on.

Ⓒ Even small children are allowed to stay up late.

Ⓓ none of the above

3. Which sentence has correct punctuation?

Ⓐ Tonya has a beautiful voice; she will sing the solo.

Ⓑ Tonya has a beautiful voice she will sing the solo.

Ⓒ Tonya has a beautiful voice she will sing; the solo.

Ⓓ none of the above

4. What is the best way to combine these two sentences? **The storm is almost over. It is still raining lightly.**

Ⓐ The storm is almost, over but it is still raining lightly.

Ⓑ The storm is almost over, but it is still raining lightly.

Ⓒ The storm is almost over but, it is still raining lightly.

Ⓓ none of the above

5. Which is an example of an irregular plural?

Ⓐ beds

Ⓒ dishes

Ⓑ geese

Ⓓ taxes

The Wind at Work • **Lesson Assessment Book 1**

The Wind at Work (continued)

Analyzing the Selection

Read the questions below. Write complete sentences for your answer. Support your answer with information from the selection.

What do you think the future of wind power is? Will people accept wind generators near their homes?

_____

_____

_____

_____

_____

_____

_____

_____

_____

_____

_____

_____

The Wind at Work (continued)

Oral Fluency Assessment

Out of Shape

As Ollie pedaled his bike, he noticed something unusual. He was climbing the short hill to his house, just as he had done a hundred times before. However, for some reason, it was taking a tremendous effort to make the bike's pedals go around. Ollie wondered, "How did I get so out of shape?"

In the driveway, he got off and pushed the bike into the garage. Ollie went into the house and got a glass of fruit juice. He called out, "Mom, I'm going to try out for the school's track team after all!"

Ollie's mother came into the kitchen and patted his shoulder. "That's wonderful, but why did you change your mind?" she inquired.

His mother listened as Ollie explained the difficulty biking home. Then she left the kitchen and disappeared for a couple of minutes. When she returned, she had a knowing smile.

"Ollie, I would love to see you go out for track, but just so you know, you're not as out of shape as you think," she said.

Puzzled, Ollie asked, "How do you know that?"

"I went out to the garage to check your bike," she answered with a chuckle. "Your tires were very low on air, so I pumped them up again. I think that the next time you pedal home, you'll feel more fit!"

Name _____ Date _____ Score _____

What Are Food Chains and Webs?

Vocabulary

Read each item. Fill in the bubble for the answer you think is correct.

1. What does the Latin root *vor* mean?

- Ⓐ to eat
- Ⓑ to breathe
- Ⓒ to see
- Ⓓ to travel

2. The word **absorbs** means

- Ⓐ stays away.
- Ⓑ takes in.
- Ⓒ lifts up.
- Ⓓ turns over.

3. A vulture is a **scavenger**. A **scavenger** is an animal that

- Ⓐ eats according to the changing seasons.
- Ⓑ feeds on plants only.
- Ⓒ eats both plants and animals.
- Ⓓ feeds on animals that are no longer alive.

4. Some grass-eating animals have **ridges** on their teeth for grinding food. **Ridges** are

- Ⓐ smooth places.
- Ⓑ colored spots.
- Ⓒ raised edges.
- Ⓓ small cracks.

5. Most meat-eating animals are **predators. Predators** are animals that

- Ⓐ feed only at night.
- Ⓑ hunt other animals for food.
- Ⓒ eat meat only during the summer.
- Ⓓ care for and feed their young.

What Are Food Chains and Webs? (continued)

Comprehension

Read the following questions carefully. Then completely fill in the bubble of each correct answer. You may look back at the selection to find the answer to each of the questions.

1. Which of these is an example of an ecosystem?

    Ⓐ a berry

    Ⓑ a chipmunk

    Ⓒ an owl

    Ⓓ a woodland

2. All of the following can be placed in the "Carnivore" category EXCEPT

    Ⓐ rabbits.

    Ⓑ tigers.

    Ⓒ lynx.

    Ⓓ weasels.

What Are Food Chains and Webs? (continued)

3. What do herbivores have in common?

(A) They are eaten by nothing else in the food web.

(B) They are the largest animals in the food chain.

(C) They are the primary consumers in the food chain.

(D) They are consumers that eat both plants and animals.

4. Why are decomposers called "nature's clean-up crew"?

(A) They are found in the water.

(B) They get rid of dead material.

(C) They prevent slime mold.

(D) They have a nice smell.

5. The selection lists sheep, cows, and deer as examples of animals that

(A) eat primarily animals.

(B) must chew their food twice.

(C) get their nutrients from the soil.

(D) use photosynthesis to feed themselves.

What Are Food Chains and Webs? (continued)

Read the following questions carefully. Use complete sentences to answer the questions.

6. What are two important things that plants provide animals and people?

   _____

   _____

7. How do meat-eating plants differ from most other plants?

   _____

   _____

8. Why is food so important to living things?

   _____

   _____

9. How is the energy from the sun passed along the food chain?

   _____

   _____

10. Why are there fewer living things on the last level of a food web or energy pyramid?

   _____

   _____

What Are Food Chains and Webs? (continued)

Read the question below. Write complete sentences for your answer. Support your answer with information from the selection.

Linking to the Concepts Why are the terms "chain" and "web" useful in describing the way food moves in and out of ecosystems?

_____

_____

_____

_____

_____

Read the question below. Your answer should be based on your own experience. Write complete sentences for your answer.

Personal Response What evidence is there of food chains and food webs in your immediate neighborhood?

_____

_____

_____

_____

_____

_____

What Are Food Chains and Webs? (continued)

Grammar, Usage, and Mechanics

Read each question. Fill in the bubble beside the answer in each group that is correct. If none of the answers is correct, choose the last answer, "none of the above."

1. In which item is a possessive noun underlined?

Ⓐ the <u>puppy's</u> basket   Ⓒ the China <u>patterns</u>

Ⓑ the <u>flowers</u> on the table Ⓓ none of the above

2. In which sentence is a possessive plural noun underlined?

Ⓐ Dozens of <u>tadpoles</u> swam in the pond.

Ⓑ The <u>tadpoles'</u> legs are starting to grow.

Ⓒ One <u>tadpole's</u> tail is almost gone.

Ⓓ none of the above

3. Which sentence contains a subject pronoun?

Ⓐ Brian wanted everyone to come to the game with him.

Ⓑ His brother, Jack, plays on the school football team.

Ⓒ They made plans to watch Jack play this Friday.

Ⓓ none of the above

4. Which sentence contains an object pronoun?

Ⓐ The quarterback threw him a long pass.

Ⓑ He caught the ball and ran for a touchdown.

Ⓒ We all cheered loudly when we won the game.

Ⓓ none of the above

5. Which of these is a compound sentence?

Ⓐ The woods were filled with fallen trees after the storm.

Ⓑ Although we were stuck, the animals leaped over the trees.

Ⓒ Workers with trucks and men with axes came to help.

Ⓓ none of the above

What Are Food Chains and Webs? (continued)

Analyzing the Selection

Read the prompt below. Write complete sentences for your response. Support your response with information from the selections.

Even though "What Are Food Chains and Webs?" is about energy, it is very different from the other selections in this unit. Explain some ways this selection is different from the others. Point out any ways you think this selection is similar to the others.

_____

_____

_____

_____

_____

_____

_____

_____

_____

_____

What Are Food Chains and Webs? (continued)

Oral Fluency Assessment

Jacob Miller's Children

Jacob Miller looked at his children playing outside their home. He was worried about their future, but knew there was almost nothing he could do about it. As a poor English farmer in the year 1564, his greatest worry was putting food on the table.

"Daydreaming again, Jacob?" Abigail Miller smiled at her husband as she kneaded the bread she would bake in the large fireplace that filled almost an entire wall. She knew that her husband was a thinker and a daydreamer. She knew that his mind often wandered.

"It saddens me to think about our children. There's not much of a life waiting for them. The boys will barely make a living farming someone else's land. The girls will marry equally poor husbands. It's a terrible shame. They are such bright children. They deserve better."

Jacob looked at his wife and smiled. She was a wonderful woman. He loved her dearly. She was the best thing that had ever happened to him. He wished he could do more for her.

"I know it sounds foolish, Abigail, but I would like the children to learn to read and write. We can't afford to send them to school, but isn't there some way they can learn their letters and numbers? It's a fine ability to have."

Name _____ **Date** _____ **Score** _____

Expository Writing

Writing Situation
A weather event you remember

Audience
Your classmates

Directions for Writing
All of us remember an interesting weather event. It might be a storm, a really cold day, or a very beautiful day. Think about an interesting weather day. Write a description of the day. Explain the type of weather and why you think it is interesting. Include details so the reader will have a good picture of the weather you are describing.

Checklist
You will earn the best score if you
- choose an interesting weather event.
- describe the event in the first paragraph.
- make sure your ideas flow in a way that makes sense.
- use sensory words and figurative language so the reader can experience the event.
- write more sentences and longer sentences when you revise.
- avoid words and phrases that are often overused.
- use correct capital letters, punctuation, and spelling.
- use subjects, verbs, and modifiers correctly.
- write complete sentences and avoid fragments or run-ons.
- read your writing after you finish and check for mistakes.

Name _____ Date _____ Score _____

. . . If You Lived at the Time of the American Revolution

Vocabulary

Read each item. Fill in the bubble for the answer you think is correct.

1. The inflectional ending **-ed** in *cooked* tells you that the action

   Ⓐ will happen soon.　　　Ⓒ is happening right now.

   Ⓑ happened in the past.　Ⓓ cannot happen.

2. **Pamphlets** are a type of

   Ⓐ organization.　　Ⓒ speech.

   Ⓑ lesson.　　　　　Ⓓ book.

3. About one-third of the people living in the colonies remained **loyal** to England. **Loyal** means that the people

   Ⓐ supported England.

   Ⓑ went to England frequently.

   Ⓒ had to pay taxes to England.

   Ⓓ wrote stories about England.

4. Some men fought with the **militia.** A **militia** is a

   Ⓐ large type of gun.

   Ⓑ group of citizens trained to fight.

   Ⓒ group of foreign soldiers.

   Ⓓ boat that takes soldiers to battle.

5. Deborah Sampson got a **discharge** from the army for her work as a soldier. This means that she got a(n)

   Ⓐ order to serve as a　　Ⓒ dismissal from service.
   　 nurse instead.

   Ⓑ large amount of money.　Ⓓ uniform.

. . . If You Lived at the Time of the American Revolution (continued)

Comprehension

Read the following questions carefully. Then completely fill in the bubble of each correct answer. You may look back at the selection to find the answer to each of the questions.

1. Which of these is not a name for the war which freed the colonies?

   Ⓐ the American Revolution

   Ⓑ the War of Independence

   Ⓒ the War of the States

   Ⓓ the Revolutionary War

2. Who were the "Lobsterbacks"?

   Ⓐ the British soldiers

   Ⓑ the Patriot militia

   Ⓒ the men behind the Boston Tea Party

   Ⓓ the Boston Massacre victims

. . . If You Lived at the Time of the American Revolution (continued)

3. Which of these was a type of business common in the Middle Colonies?

   Ⓐ shipbuilding

   Ⓑ farming

   Ⓒ fishing

   Ⓓ whale hunting

4. What caused the Boston Tea Party?

   Ⓐ There was too much tea in the Colonies.

   Ⓑ It was a celebration after the states declared their freedom.

   Ⓒ The Loyalists were celebrating a popular British holiday.

   Ⓓ There was a tax on tea paid to the British.

5. What happened right after the Boston Massacre?

   Ⓐ The Stamp Act was repealed.

   Ⓑ The Declaration of Independence was signed.

   Ⓒ New York City became known as the Tory capital of America.

   Ⓓ Many people joined the Patriots.

. . . If You Lived at the Time of the American Revolution (continued)

Read the following questions carefully. Use complete sentences to answer the questions.

6. Why is the Fourth of July a holiday?

_____

_____

7. What is the difference between a Loyalist and a Patriot?

_____

_____

8. Name two reasons the author gives as to why people stayed loyal to England.

_____

_____

9. How was Benjamin Franklin different from his son, William?

_____

_____

10. Why did Deborah Sampson dress in men's clothes and change her name to Robert Shurtleff?

_____

_____

. . . If You Lived at the Time of the American Revolution (continued)

Read the question below. Write complete sentences for your answer. Support your answer with information from the selection.

Linking to the Concepts How did the Declaration of Independence change the lives of the colonists?

_____

_____

_____

_____

_____

Read the question below. Your answer should be based on your own experience. Write complete sentences for your answer.

Personal Response Would you have joined the Patriots, or would you have remained loyal to the king? Explain your answer.

_____

_____

_____

_____

_____

. . . If You Lived at the Time of the American Revolution (continued)

Grammar, Usage, and Mechanics

Read each question. Fill in the bubble beside the answer in each group that is correct. If none of the answers is correct, choose the last answer, "none of the above."

1. Which sentence contains a comparative adjective?

Ⓐ Those men are the ones he told you about yesterday.

Ⓑ Riga and Olga have both just turned twenty years old.

Ⓒ The dinosaur skeleton was taller than us.

Ⓓ none of the above

2. Which sentence contains an adjective that tells *how many?*

Ⓐ My brother had eight candles on his birthday cake.

Ⓑ The rainbow made colorful patterns in the clouds.

Ⓒ That paintbrush is the best one to use on the trim.

Ⓓ none of the above

3. Which sentence contains an adjective that tells *which kind?*

Ⓐ Snow White lived with the seven dwarves.

Ⓑ These pears are yellow, while the others are green.

Ⓒ The tired hikers rested for a while.

Ⓓ none of the above

4. In which sentence does the adverb modify a verb?

Ⓐ Jenna felt slightly tired.　　Ⓒ The glass was almost empty.

Ⓑ The spy walked carefully.　Ⓓ none of the above

5. In which sentence does the adverb modify an adjective?

Ⓐ When coach spoke the team listened closely.

Ⓑ The captain shouted loudly.

Ⓒ Last summer, the South had unusually dry weather.

Ⓓ none of the above

. . . If You Lived at the Time of the American Revolution (continued)

Analyzing the Selection

Read the questions below. Write complete sentences for your answer. Support your answer with information from the selection.

How do you think the American people felt during the Revolutionary War? Keep in mind that most people had little news of the fighting and did not know how the war was going. Do you think that everyday life continued more or less normally?

_____

_____

_____

_____

_____

_____

_____

_____

_____

_____

_____

. . . If You Lived at the Time of the American Revolution (continued)

Oral Fluency Assessment

Golf: A Silly Game?

The bus came to a stop in the parking lot of the golf course. A group of students got off and walked to the meeting area. Carla Morgan, their teacher's sister, was standing there with a few golfers. The children lined up quietly and stared at the group of golfers. Among them was Hoop Landers, a professional basketball player they all had seen on television.

Carla introduced all of the players. Then she divided up the children into small groups. Alice, Steven, Edward, and two others quickly ran over to be with Hoop. He was about to start teaching when Steven spoke up.

"Mr. Landers, how come you're here? Do you like golf? Isn't it a silly game compared to basketball or football?"

Hoop looked at Steven's name tag. Then he said, "Steven, there's no such thing as a silly game if you have the right attitude. I love basketball, but I started playing golf a few years ago so I could spend time with my parents. Here, give it a try."

The children followed Hoop's directions. Pretty soon they were all making good swings. Steven was surprised to see that Alice could hit the ball at least as far as he could. He could not help but think that maybe golf was not such a silly game after all.

Name _____ Date _____ Score _____

The Midnight Ride of Paul Revere

Vocabulary

Read each item. Fill in the bubble for the answer you think is correct.

1. A **gleam** is a

    Ⓐ small mountain.   Ⓒ horse.

    Ⓑ battleship.   Ⓓ flash of light.

2. What is the meaning of the suffix *-less?*

    Ⓐ action or process   Ⓒ one who does

    Ⓑ without   Ⓓ state of

3. He held the lantern **aloft.** That means he held it

    Ⓐ with both hands.

    Ⓑ near the ground.

    Ⓒ behind his back.

    Ⓓ high above the ground.

4. Paul Revere rode on a **ledge.** A **ledge** is

    Ⓐ a narrow surface.

    Ⓑ a covered wagon.

    Ⓒ a special kind of saddle.

    Ⓓ a large breed of horse.

5. Paul Revere **spread** the word about the British. In this sentence, **spread** means to

    Ⓐ make something known.

    Ⓑ guide someone.

    Ⓒ create something new.

    Ⓓ give shelter to someone.

The Midnight Ride of Paul Revere (continued)

Comprehension

Read the following questions carefully. Then completely fill in the bubble of each correct answer. You may look back at the selection to find the answer to each of the questions.

1. "The Midnight Ride of Paul Revere" was written from the third-person point of view of someone who
   - (A) was sent to warn the militia that the British were coming.
   - (B) was reporting the event for a newspaper.
   - (C) was a British soldier.
   - (D) was alive a long time after the event occurred.

2. When did Revere ride?
   - (A) April 18, 1875
   - (B) after the battle of Lexington and Concord
   - (C) April 18, 1775
   - (D) after the Declaration of Independence was signed

The Midnight Ride of Paul Revere (continued)

3. Which of these was NOT something Revere did?

  Ⓐ He signed the Declaration of Independence.

  Ⓑ He helped plan the Boston Tea Party.

  Ⓒ He spied on British troop movement around Boston.

  Ⓓ He carried news to and from the Continental Congress.

4. What does Revere's friend see as he first looks down from the church tower?

  Ⓐ the bay

  Ⓑ British troops

  Ⓒ a graveyard

  Ⓓ two lanterns

5. Where did the first battle of the Revolution actually take place?

  Ⓐ Boston

  Ⓑ Lexington

  Ⓒ New York City

  Ⓓ Concord

The Midnight Ride of Paul Revere (continued)

Read the following questions carefully. Use complete sentences to answer the questions.

6. What is Revere's friend doing near the barracks door?

_____

_____

7. What is the difference between what the poem and the historical note say about where the signal lanterns were hung?

_____

_____

8. Why did the British think they would have an easy time defeating the militia in Concord?

_____

_____

9. What is the difference between what happened to Revere in the poem and in the historical note?

_____

_____

10. What happened after the fighting stopped in Lexington?

_____

_____

The Midnight Ride of Paul Revere (continued)

Read the question below. Write complete sentences for your answer. Support your answer with information from the selection.

Linking to the Concepts Why was spreading the news about the British so important?

_____

_____

_____

_____

_____

Read the prompt below. Your response should be based on your own experience. Write complete sentences for your response.

Personal Response Think about what Paul Revere did. Write about something you did that was part of a bigger event involving other people.

_____

_____

_____

_____

_____

The Midnight Ride of Paul Revere (continued)

Grammar, Usage, and Mechanics

Read each question. Fill in the bubble beside the answer in each group that is correct. If none of the answers is correct, choose the last answer, "none of the above."

1. In which sentence is a preposition underlined?

   Ⓐ Put it on the <u>table</u>. Ⓒ <u>Put</u> it on the table.

   Ⓑ Put it <u>on</u> the table. Ⓓ none of the above

2. In which sentence is a prepositional phrase underlined?

   Ⓐ The sea lion <u>in the tank</u> is part of the show.

   Ⓑ The sea lion in the tank <u>is part</u> of the show.

   Ⓒ The <u>sea lion in</u> the tank is part of the show.

   Ⓓ none of the above

3. In which sentence is the object of the preposition underlined?

   Ⓐ Dayton painted a picture early <u>in</u> the morning.

   Ⓑ Dayton painted a picture <u>early</u> in the morning.

   Ⓒ Dayton painted a picture early in the <u>morning</u>.

   Ⓓ none of the above

4. Which sentence contains a prepositional phrase?

   Ⓐ My brother does not like thunder and lightning.

   Ⓑ Paul wondered how electricity works.

   Ⓒ Ben Franklin flew a kite when it stormed.

   Ⓓ none of the above

5. In this sentence, which word is modified by a prepositional phrase?

   The boys in their tiny red caps ran in the woods.

   Ⓐ tiny Ⓒ caps

   Ⓑ red Ⓓ none of the above

The Midnight Ride of Paul Revere (continued)

Analyzing the Selection

Read the questions below. Write complete sentences for your answer. Support your answer with information from the selection.

What are the most important differences between the poem "The Midnight Ride of Paul Revere" and what actually happened? Why do you think Longfellow changed the actual story?

_____

_____

_____

_____

_____

_____

_____

_____

_____

_____

_____

_____

The Midnight Ride of Paul Revere (continued)

Oral Fluency Assessment

Gertrude Ederle

Thousands of people cross between France and England every day. They take planes, ferries, and even trains. An American athlete, Gertrude Ederle, used a different method. She was the first woman to swim across the English Channel.

Ederle was born in New York City in 1906. She started swimming at an early age. Soon she was on her way to becoming one of the most famous swimmers of her time. When she was sixteen, Ederle broke seven records in one day at a meet. Two years later, in 1924, she swam in the Olympics. She won a gold medal in the 400-meter freestyle relay.

After the Olympics, she looked for an even greater test. One of the hardest swims in the world is the twenty-one mile English Channel. The seas in the channel can be rough. The water is cold. In the past, only male swimmers had made the swim.

Most people believed the swim was too difficult for a woman. Ederle wanted to prove them wrong. She did not make it on her first attempt. In 1926, she tried again.

She started from France. Ederle had to swim farther than planned because of heavy seas. She went an extra distance. She still managed to beat the world record by almost two hours. This feat made her famous at the age of twenty.

Name _____ Date _____ Score _____

The Master Spy of Yorktown

Vocabulary

Read each item. Fill in the bubble for the answer you think is correct.

1. The base word in **commander** is

Ⓐ command.　　　Ⓒ man.

Ⓑ er.　　　Ⓓ com.

2. **Idle** means the same as

Ⓐ a little late.　　　Ⓒ not busy.

Ⓑ very fast.　　　Ⓓ perfect.

3. According to Thomas Jefferson, Virginia was a state of "mild laws and a people not used to **prompt** obedience." This means that the people

Ⓐ paid their taxes on time every year.

Ⓑ were not quick to follow orders.

Ⓒ did not own much land.

Ⓓ worked hard to make a living.

4. The British were **looting** and burning their way through Virginia. This means that the British were

Ⓐ learning how to herd sheep.

Ⓑ stealing valuable things.

Ⓒ growing crops.

Ⓓ riding a train.

5. Lafayette tried to keep up the morale of Virginia **civilians.** **Civilians** are

Ⓐ people who are not in the military.　　　Ⓒ students.

Ⓑ tobacco farmers.　　　Ⓓ traveling preachers.

The Master Spy of Yorktown (continued)

Comprehension

Read the following questions carefully. Then completely fill in the bubble of each correct answer. You may look back at the selection to find the answer to each of the questions.

1. Which of these is a fact about the Marquis de Lafayette?
   - (A) He was from France.
   - (B) He was a good commander.
   - (C) He was very intelligent.
   - (D) He was excited to be asked to command an army.

2. Why was Lafayette having a difficult time in Virginia?
   - (A) He could not find the British army.
   - (B) His army was so large that it was difficult to keep everyone informed.
   - (C) The people living there were not very helpful
   - (D) He did not have enough American money.

The Master Spy of Yorktown (continued)

3. Who was James Armistead?

(A) a British commander

(B) a naval hero

(C) an American spy

(D) a French nobleman

4. What happened after Cornwallis's army arrived in Portsmouth?

(A) The soldiers built defenses immediately.

(B) General Arnold was almost captured by a band of Virginia soldiers.

(C) Armistead became a trusted servant of Cornwallis.

(D) A fleet of ships came to anchor in the harbor.

5. Why did Cornwallis surrender?

(A) He and his army were surrounded.

(B) Most of his men were dead.

(C) He and his army ran out of supplies.

(D) Most of his men were ill.

The Master Spy of Yorktown (continued)

Read the following questions carefully. Use complete sentences to answer the questions.

6. Why was Lafayette excited about commanding an American force?

_____

_____

7. Why was General Cornwallis so careful with his papers?

_____

_____

8. Why was Cornwallis surprised to see Armistead in an American uniform?

_____

_____

9. Why did James Armistead change his name to Lafayette?

_____

_____

10. How was Saul Matthews like James Armistead?

_____

_____

The Master Spy of Yorktown (continued)

Read the question below. Write complete sentences for your answer. Support your answer with information from the selection.

Linking to the Concepts What type of person do you think Armistead was? Use information from the selection and your own opinion.

_____

_____

_____

_____

Read the questions below. Your answer should be based on your own experience. Write complete sentences for your answer.

Personal Response If you had been Armistead, would you have done the things he did? Why or why not?

_____

_____

_____

_____

_____

The Master Spy of Yorktown (continued)

Grammar, Usage, and Mechanics

Read each question. Fill in the bubble beside the answer in each group that is correct. If none of the answers is correct, choose the last answer, "none of the above."

1. Which computer command would you use to remove a word from a document?

   Ⓐ cut   Ⓒ select

   Ⓑ paste   Ⓓ none of the above

2. Before you copy a word, what must you do?

   Ⓐ delete the word

   Ⓑ close the document

   Ⓒ select the word

   Ⓓ none of the above

3. When you move a word from one place to another in a document, what is it called?

   Ⓐ move or not

   Ⓑ try to change

   Ⓒ cut and paste

   Ⓓ none of the above

4. When you have finished working on a document you would like to use in the future, what should you do?

   Ⓐ delete it   Ⓒ explain it

   Ⓑ save it   Ⓓ none of the above

5. What is it called when you use the cursor to identify some words in a document?

   Ⓐ exchanging   Ⓒ highlighting

   Ⓑ replacing   Ⓓ none of the above

The Master Spy of Yorktown (continued)

Analyzing the Selection

Read the questions below. Write complete sentences for your answer. Support your answer with information from the selections.

Think about Armistead and the other people you read about in this unit. What did they think about the future of the new country? Do you think they had high hopes, or were they unsure? Use information from the selection and your own opinions.

_____

_____

_____

_____

_____

_____

_____

_____

_____

_____

The Master Spy of Yorktown (continued)

Oral Fluency Assessment

Eddie and Gramps

Eddie's grandfather did not live in a regular house. He needed special nursing care. Eddie was sad that his grandfather could not stay with his family in their house. His mom and dad said that they could not give him the help that he needed. Eddie understood, but he did not like it.

The place where Eddie's grandfather lived was called "Elder Care Nursing Home." It was not an elegant place, but it was home to a lot of nice people. Eddie tried to visit his grandfather as often as he could. They had a great relationship. Sometimes they would play checkers or cards. Mostly, though, they would just talk.

Eddie was a quiet boy. He usually kept to himself. He spoke very softly. His grandfather was his best friend. They both enjoyed each other's company.

Eddie's grandfather—"Gramps" as Eddie called him—had lived a very exciting life. It was amazing to hear of all the things he had done. Among other things, he had been a soldier in the army, a firefighter, and a mason. His stories were always great. They made Eddie think. When Gramps started telling stories of his past, Eddie realized that he was lucky to have him in his life.

Name _____ Date _____ Score _____

Shh! We're Writing the Constitution

Vocabulary

Read each item. Fill in the bubble for the answer you think is correct.

1. What does the prefix **con-** mean?

   Ⓐ before   Ⓒ too much

   Ⓑ change from   Ⓓ with

2. An **accomplishment** is an

   Ⓐ observation.   Ⓒ illness.

   Ⓑ achievement.   Ⓓ escape.

3. George Washington wanted his troops to swear **allegiance** to the United States. In this sentence, **allegiance** means

   Ⓐ faithful support.

   Ⓑ lasting glory.

   Ⓒ money and funds.

   Ⓓ extra time.

4. Washington hoped to see the states united under one **central** government. In this sentence, **central** means

   Ⓐ elected.   Ⓒ hard-working.

   Ⓑ main.   Ⓓ caring.

5. Each state legislature sent **delegates** to the Continental Congress. **Delegates** are

   Ⓐ people chosen to act for others.

   Ⓑ extra supplies.

   Ⓒ tax money.

   Ⓓ copies of the state's laws.

Shh! We're Writing the Constitution (continued)

Comprehension

Read the following questions carefully. Then completely fill in the bubble of each correct answer. You may look back at the selection to find the answer to each of the questions.

1. Why did the First Continental Congress meet?

   Ⓐ The country needed some type of government.

   Ⓑ The states were concerned about British rule.

   Ⓒ The states badly wanted a strong national government.

   Ⓓ The states needed to raise taxes.

2. Which of these was NOT a reason delegates gave for being late to the convention?

   Ⓐ They did not have enough money.

   Ⓑ The roads were muddy.

   Ⓒ They had personal business to attend to.

   Ⓓ The British Army was advancing.

Shh! We're Writing the Constitution (continued)

3. Which of these is an opinion about James Madison?

Ⓐ Madison arrived in Philadelphia eleven days early.

Ⓑ Madison sat in the front of the room.

Ⓒ Madison was worked up about the meeting.

Ⓓ Madison was never absent for a session.

4. Which of these is a fact about Edmund Randolph?

Ⓐ Randolph was the governor of Virginia.

Ⓑ Randolph was likable.

Ⓒ Randolph was handsome.

Ⓓ Randolph did not say alarming things.

5. The author wrote this piece in order to

Ⓐ explain the Constitution to the readers.

Ⓑ convince readers that Thomas Jefferson was a great writer.

Ⓒ tell about how the Constitution came to be.

Ⓓ show that early Americans did not trust people from other states.

Shh! We're Writing the Constitution (continued)

Read the following questions carefully. Use complete sentences to answer the questions.

6. After the Revolutionary War, why were most people in America not ready to call themselves Americans?

_____

_____

7. What was the first thing the convention delegates did?

_____

_____

8. Why were the windows of the meeting house kept closed although it was hot outside?

_____

_____

9. What was the Virginia Plan?

_____

_____

10. What was Alexander Hamilton's opinion about the president's term of office?

_____

_____

Shh! We're Writing the Constitution (continued)

Read the question below. Write complete sentences for your answer. Support your answer with information from the selection.

Linking to the Concepts What might have happened had the states remained "sovereign"?

_____

_____

_____

_____

_____

Read the questions below. Your answer should be based on your own experience. Write complete sentences for your answer.

Personal Response How would you have felt if you were helping to write the Constitution? Would you be able to work easily with the other people?

_____

_____

_____

_____

_____

Shh! We're Writing the Constitution (continued)

Grammar, Usage, and Mechanics

Read each question. Fill in the bubble beside the answer in each group that is correct. If none of the answers is correct, choose the last answer, "none of the above."

1. Which sentence has correct capitalization?

Ⓐ Raul writes for *Popular Mechanics* magazine.

Ⓑ Raul writes for *Popular mechanics* magazine.

Ⓒ raul writes for *popular mechanics* magazine.

Ⓓ none of the above

2. Which sentence has a mistake in capitalization?

Ⓐ Have you seen *Bambi* on DVD?

Ⓑ Gary Paulsen is the author of *Hatchet*.

Ⓒ The House of Representatives is in session now.

Ⓓ none of the above

3. Which item has correct capitalization?

Ⓐ Winter in Palm Beach, Florida Ⓒ winter in Palm Beach, Florida

Ⓑ Winter in palm Beach, Florida Ⓓ none of the above

4. Which sentence has correct capitalization?

Ⓐ Driving through south Dakota, we saw many farms.

Ⓑ People visit new York to see the Statue of Liberty.

Ⓒ The airline has a new price for trips to europe.

Ⓓ none of the above

5. Which sentence has a mistake in capitalization?

Ⓐ Uncle ned took his nephews to a beach in Maryland.

Ⓑ The plane stopped in Poland, Denmark, and Greenland.

Ⓒ Dr. Liu came here from Asia about ten years ago.

Ⓓ none of the above

Shh! We're Writing the Constitution (continued)

Analyzing the Selection

Read the questions below. Write complete sentences for your answer. Support your answer with information from the selection.

Not many people know how difficult it was to write the Constitution. What were some of the challenges that the delegates faced, and how did they resolve them? What did you find most surprising about the process?

_____

_____

_____

_____

_____

_____

_____

_____

_____

_____

_____

_____

_____

Shh! We're Writing the Constitution (continued)

Oral Fluency Assessment

Cathy Is a Big Help

Michael did not know much about cars, especially how they are constructed. That is why Cathy suggested that she help him. Cathy grew up working with her father. Her family's garage was like a workshop and her father was always building or fixing something. Cathy was right beside him, helping him out whether he liked it or not. He made cabinets and shelves for her mother and built a dollhouse for Cathy. And her father was always working on his classic car.

Cathy got pretty good with tools and knowing how things work, especially with cars. She liked to think that her dad's car would have never been wheeled out of the garage without her help.

The big race was called "The Little Grand Prix of Clintonville." The rules were simple. The entry had to be a two-person car made out of wood and metal. It had to have four wheels and be powered only by gravity. The race took place down a hill.

Cathy had run into Michael while walking to the store.

"Come on, Michael," Cathy said. "You and I could build the best car out there."

On the way back, Cathy was very excited about the whole thing and thought that she and Michael would make a wonderful, and winning, team.

Name _____ Date _____ Score _____

Give Me Liberty!

Vocabulary

Read each item. Fill in the bubble for the answer you think is correct.

1. A **declaration** is a type of

   Ⓐ question.   Ⓒ honor.

   Ⓑ concern.   Ⓓ statement.

2. What is the superlative form of the adjective **good?**

   Ⓐ betterest   Ⓒ better

   Ⓑ best   Ⓓ goodest

3. British warships **bombarded** the seaport of Charleston, South Carolina. In this sentence, **bombarded** means

   Ⓐ attacked with heavy fire. Ⓒ crowded inside.

   Ⓑ surrounded completely. Ⓓ steered clear of.

4. Congress held its final **debate** on the idea of independence. A **debate** is a(n)

   Ⓐ election between two or more candidates.

   Ⓑ rough draft of a written document.

   Ⓒ discussion between groups that disagree.

   Ⓓ open trial with a judge and a jury.

5. People worried that seeking independence would be like **exposing** a new family before they found another shelter. In this sentence, **exposing** means

   Ⓐ trying to prove something is right.

   Ⓑ leaving something unprotected.

   Ⓒ looking for something that does not exist.

   Ⓓ giving up something for the benefit of all.

Give Me Liberty! (continued)

Comprehension

Read the following questions carefully. Then completely fill in the bubble of each correct answer. You may look back at the selection to find the answer to each of the questions.

1. What happened right after the final version of the Declaration of Independence was voted on and approved unanimously?

   Ⓐ Copies were carried by express to the villages.

   Ⓑ A boy at the door gave a signal for bells to ring.

   Ⓒ All members of Congress signed the form.

   Ⓓ A copy was sent by ship to King George.

2. The statement "The delegates who favored independence got busy behind the scenes" suggests that they

   Ⓐ worked together to persuade the other delegates.

   Ⓑ helped Jefferson with his draft of the declaration.

   Ⓒ asked Adams to give a speech.

   Ⓓ leaked negative information to the newspapers.

Give Me Liberty! (continued)

3. The author says that Jefferson "squirmed in his seat" while Congress worked on his draft. This phrase suggests that Jefferson was

   Ⓐ bored with the meeting.

   Ⓑ shy about what he had written.

   Ⓒ uncomfortable with the process.

   Ⓓ eager to get to another appointment.

4. What made the delegates want to vote quickly on July 4th?

   Ⓐ The summer heat was unbearable.

   Ⓑ The colonies were demanding freedom.

   Ⓒ The assembly room was filled with horseflies.

   Ⓓ The noise outside the statehouse door was distracting.

5. At this point in his career, Jefferson was all of the following EXCEPT

   Ⓐ a scholar.

   Ⓑ a writer.

   Ⓒ a delegate.

   Ⓓ a president.

Give Me Liberty! (continued)

**Read the following questions carefully. Use complete
sentences to answer the questions.**

6. What are some of the reasons Adams believed
Jefferson was the better man to draft the Declaration
of Independence?

_____

_____

7. According to the selection, what sources did Jefferson
draw upon while writing his draft?

_____

_____

8. What did the delegates risk by signing the Declaration
of Independence?

_____

_____

9. Why did John Hancock make his signature so large?

_____

_____

10. What did Jefferson state was the purpose of the
Declaration of Independence?

_____

_____

Give Me Liberty! (continued)

Read the question below. Write complete sentences for your answer. Support your answer with information from the selection.

Linking to the Concepts How are the ideas of equality and the rights to life, liberty and the pursuit of happiness still important today?

_____

_____

_____

_____

_____

Read the question below. Your answer should be based on your own experience. Write complete sentences for your answer.

Personal Response Imagine you were Thomas Jefferson. How would you have responded to the edits or comments about the draft you had written?

_____

_____

_____

_____

_____

_____

Give Me Liberty! (continued)

Grammar, Usage, and Mechanics

Read each question. Fill in the bubble beside the answer in each group that is correct. If none of the answers is correct, choose the last answer, "none of the above."

1. In which sentence is the adverb used correctly?

   Ⓐ On our team, Pat moves more quicker than Len.

   Ⓑ On our team, Pat moves quicker than Len.

   Ⓒ On our team, Pat quicker most moves than Len.

   Ⓓ none of the above

2. In which sentence is the adjective used correctly?

   Ⓐ Tyrone won a prize for the liveliest presentation.

   Ⓑ Tyrone won a prize for the most liveliest presentation.

   Ⓒ Tyrone won a prize for the most livelier presentation.

   Ⓓ none of the above

3. In which sentence is a preposition underlined?

   Ⓐ Everyone in the talent <u>show</u> gets a turn on the stage.

   Ⓑ <u>Everyone</u> in the talent show gets a turn on the stage.

   Ⓒ Everyone in the talent show gets a turn <u>on</u> the stage.

   Ⓓ none of the above

4. In which sentence is a prepositional phrase underlined?

   Ⓐ A tiger's striped coat lets it blend <u>into the forest</u>.

   Ⓑ A tiger's <u>striped coat</u> lets it blend into the forest.

   Ⓒ A tiger's striped coat <u>lets it blend</u> into the forest.

   Ⓓ none of the above

5. What would you use to move text in a document?

   Ⓐ spell-check   Ⓒ save

   Ⓑ cut and paste   Ⓓ none of the above

Give Me Liberty! (continued)

Analyzing the Selection

Read the questions below. Write complete sentences for your answer. Support your answer with information from the selections.

More than anything else, the American Revolution was successful because the people involved were motivated to make a new country. Why were they so driven? What made them willing to take on the strongest country in the world at the time? Use information from the selections as well as your opinion and prior knowledge.

_____

_____

_____

_____

_____

_____

_____

_____

_____

_____

Give Me Liberty! (continued)

Oral Fluency Assessment

Silk

Many years ago, the Chinese discovered a secret. Boiling the cocoons of a type of caterpillar called a silkworm gave them long, unbroken threads. When this thread was woven, the cloth was soft and shiny. They called it silk.

At first they gathered the cocoons in the wild. This wild silk often had holes in it or tiny marks. Later they began raising the worms on their own farms. If these silkworms were kept in special trays, the thread would be unmarked.

Taking care of silkworms was not easy. Before they spin their cocoons, silkworms eat constantly. A village worked day and night to gather enough mulberry leaves to feed the silkworms. Cocoons had to be boiled. If they did not boil them, the moths poked holes in them. All this work made silk costly.

Because it was tightly woven, soldiers realized silk could stop arrows. They wore silk under their armor. During World War I, silk was used to make bulletproof vests. Parachutes and tires can also be made of silk. Chinese doctors even used silk to make new veins for people. Though it is soft and beautiful, silk is also strong, so it is used for many things besides fancy clothing.

Name _____ **Date** _____ **Score** _____

Persuasive Writing

Writing Situation
The most important event in early American history

Audience
Your classmates

Directions for Writing
Many important events happened around the time of the American Revolution. Which one do you think was most important? Describe the event and explain why you think it was important. Write in a way that will convince the reader that your opinion is sound.

Checklist
You will earn the best score if you
- choose an event you know well and think is important.
- plan your writing before you begin.
- state your point of view clearly in the first paragraph.
- include facts or examples that support your point of view.
- mention the historic event several times.
- use words that tell how you feel about the event.
- explain the event clearly to your readers.
- avoid words and phrases that are often overused.
- vary your sentences and the words you use.
- choose words that are strong, colorful, and accurately express your ideas.